AI

ABOUT THE AUTHOR

Robin Richards was a free-lance writer. He worked for 45 years as a civil servant in Cardiff after spending three and a half years in the Royal Navy during the last war. He is founder editor of 'Limited Edition' a Company House newspaper for staff in Cardiff, London and Edinburgh. He contributed to the 'Guardian', 'Toronto Star', 'BBC Wales', 'Brandon Sun', 'Western Mail' and 'Daily Post'.

TWO BRIDGES
OVER MENAI

Robin Richards

First edition: 1996
New and revised edition: 2004

© Text: Robin Richards

Copyright © by Gwasg Carreg Gwalch 1996.

ISBN: 0-86381-834-X

Published by
Gwasg Carreg Gwalch,
12 Iard yr Orsaf, Llanrwst, Wales, LL26 0EH.
Tel: 01492 642031   Fax: 01492 641502
Printed and published in Wales.

From Taid to:
Ceri (in Canada), Megan and Rhys

My grateful thanks to:
The Rt. Hon. Lord Cledwyn of Penrhos, P.C., C.H.
Mr R.B. Daimond, Director of Highways, Gwynedd County Council
Mr Wynne Jones, Assistant Director of Highways, Gwynedd County Council
Mr Graham A. Bonner, Group Engineer, Gwynedd County Council
Mr K.A.S. Fletcher, Town Clerk, Welshpool Town Council
Eva Bredsdorff, Powysland Museum, Welshpool
Sir Alexander Gibb & Partners, Cardiff
Driver and Vehicle Licensing Agency
R. Aled Richards, Cardiff

The two Menai bridges (Gwynedd Archives Service)

CONTENTS

FOREWORD

The original edition of this book was published before the work on the Britannia railway bridge was fully completed following the devastating fire on Saturday, 23rd May, 1970.

It was too early at the time to consider all the advantages of another crossing of Afon Menai *(Menai Strait)*. This revised edition gives us the opportunity to do so.

In preparing the revised edition of this book it was important to find the effect the new access to the island the Britannia roadway is having on traffic.

The benefits have been tremendous. Heavy vehicles come over without hold-up on Britannia – except of course when delayed by high winds.

Touring coaches use the bridge and park a short way down the A5 road back to Porthaethwy *(Menai Bridge)*. Tourists are now able to see Telford's suspension bridge against the magnificent backdrop of the mountains of Snowdonia.

Looking at DVLC Swansea statistics from 1989 to 1994 comparison of traffic is stable over the years. Pont y Borth *(the Menai Suspension Bridge)* carries 40% of the total traffic and the Britannia bridge 60% (not counting its rail traffic).

In numerical terms the total for both bridges is 428,062.

Robin Richards,
Llandudno
July 1996

Thomas Telford

THE SUSPENSION BRIDGE

BEFORE ANY BRIDGE WAS BUILT

There was a time when water flowed through Afon Menai *(Menai Strait)*, from Caernarfon to Beaumaris, without the shadow of any bridge across it. The only way to get from one side to another was by ferry boat. Cattle and pigs swam across.

The town, which sits on granite with pine woods around it, was not called by the English Menai Bridge, but Porthaethwy. It was a hustling landing place with over 300 sailing ships passing through the Strait. Some called to land cargoes from Liverpool or even more distant ports. Porthaethwy was a good landing place, where goods could be sent into the island of Môn *(Anglesey)*.

Thomas Pennant in his book *Tours in Wales* says:

'Porthaethwy, the most general ferry into Anglesey, is immediately below the church. The passage of cattle at this place is very great: I cannot enumerate them; but it is computed that the island sends forth annually from twelve to fifteen thousand head, multitudes of sheep and hogs . . .

From the same authority it appears, that in 1770 upwards of ninety thousand bushels of corn were exported.'

Porthaethwy had its share of pirates and smugglers who made full use of the quiet, wooded coves to slip past the watchful Customs and Excise officials.

A book published in 1883, called *Tours in Wales* by Thomas Pennant (edited by John Rhys, Professor of Celtic at Oxford) contains an interesting reference to Porthaethwy being a place where slaves were sold up to the 15th Century.

Porthaethwy's importance grew from its position on the A5 London to Holyhead road as the Irish traffic increased. The journey from London in 1780 by stagecoach took 3 days and it was the narrow crossing of the Menai Strait which was feared most of all.

Tired travellers arrived at the Bangor side of the Strait, and they and their luggage were transferred to a ferry boat. It was grim in winter for women and children, for many a ferry boat had been carried down the strait in a swirling spring tide. If the weather was calm the journey took 45 minutes.

In 1800, times were hard and the ferry boat men were unscrupulous in their methods. Their charges at the beginning of the trip were one shilling a person which was exorbitant. This got the passengers into the boats, but when they had left the shore, the price went up. Passengers were terrorised into paying much more.

Cattle and pigs were made to swim across in two stages. Those which survived the sucking whirlpools rested on a rock called 'Ynys y Moch', (Pig Island), before being forced to swim the remaining distance to the Caernarfonshire side. Ynys y Moch is the present site of the western pier of the Suspension Bridge.

Telford's original pully-blocks used in the
construction of the bridge in 1825

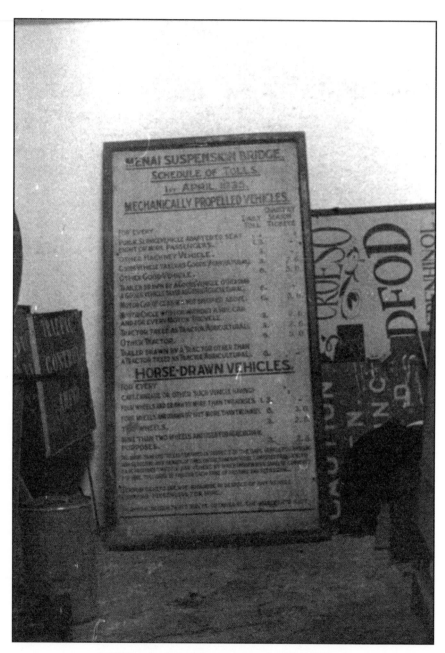

A 1935 price board for crossing the Menai Strait

OPPOSITION TO THE BRIDGE

Roads from London to Holyhead in 1800 were so appalling it was not long before travellers' difficulties were being raised in the House of Commons.

The Irish Members of Parliament were particularly active. While the route as a whole was criticised, everyone spoke about the particular difficulties of the crossing of the Menai Strait. The Secretary of State for Ireland was pressed *'to end this national scandal'*.

The Secretary of State was sympathetic, but replied that the cost of bridging the Menai Strait was prohibitive. The Government had been considering this particular difficulty for some time. In 1776, a Mr Goldborne proposed an embankment from each shore with a bridge in the middle. In 1785, a Mr Nichols suggested a wooden viaduct with a drawbridge in the centre. This was to be built at Cadnant Island, a place about a quarter of a mile towards Bangor from the present site.

By 1810 a commission was set up to enquire into the state of the roads between Shrewsbury, Chester and Caergybi *(Holyhead)*. Thomas Telford was asked to look at the Menai Strait and report as to the most effective way of bridging its treacherous waters.

There were many people in 1800 who did not want a bridge built over the Menai Strait. They were, in the main, those whose livelihood was threatened – ferry owners, local shipping interests, even local gentry with aesthetic objections. They all appeared before the Commission set up to hear objections.

Two local pilots, John Jones and John Thomas, thought a bridge of the size proposed would, *'Play tricks with the wind and tide and make piloting ships impossible'*. This seemed to be a valid objection because these sailors risked their lives going through the swirling Swellies.

Ferry owners naturally objected to their livelihood being taken away. The most important of the six ferries crossing the Strait was at Porthaethwy, owned by Miss Jane Williams of Conwy.

It was natural too, that trade interests, who would find traffic going away from their areas, objected. On 14th August, 1818, a

13

meeting took place in the Town Hall, Caernarfon, of local gentry, the Marquis of Anglesey, Owen Williams of Craig y Don, T. Ashton Smith and local tradesmen. There was uproar at the idea of having a bridge seven miles down the Strait from Caernarfon. Their trade and livelihood was threatened. Their objections were, however, to no avail.

Menai Bridge, the entrance

START OF CONSTRUCTION

At last the Commission was satisfied that bridging the Menai Strait was a practical proposition and recommended to the Lords of His Majesty's Treasury a grant of £20,000 for work to begin.

Thomas Telford was appointed principal engineer with Mr William Alexander Provis as resident engineer.

While Telford had thought hard about the problem of crossing the Strait and proposed two bridges, neither was used. What was used was a third choice, a suspension bridge built on the lines he had suggested for another place, the Runcorn Gap on the River Mersey.

Thomas Telford had looked at the Menai Strait from Beaumaris to Caernarfon and took account of the cost limits allowed.

The first suggested bridge was the one Telford favoured most. It would cost £127,331, while the second was more expensive at £158,698, and was planned for a site nearer Caernarfon than the present bridge. The design had five arches, three of cast iron and two of stone.

Telford first proposed a cast iron arch of 500 feet span with the crown of the arch to be 100 feet above the high water mark of spring tides. The width of the roadway was to be 40 feet. Telford used this design when he built the bridge over the Spey at Craigellachie between Elgin and Dufftown 8 years previously. Why was this proposal not accepted?

There was one great difficulty in holding up the arch while it was being built. Telford argued that this was possible if instead of supporting the arch from below, it was suspended from above while being constructed. This was a revolutionary idea. How was the arch to be held from above?

It could be done by building two frames, each 50 feet high – one on each main pier. The arch could be built out from each side and held from above, by a long chain running back to the 50 feet high frames. Once the arch was completed it became self-supporting.

There is no reason to suppose, that, had Telford been allowed to go ahead with this method, he would not have been successful. A similar method was used years later by Marc Isambard Brunel.

Many thought that this ingenious method of supporting arches, whilst they are being constructed, was Brunel's, but credit must go to Thomas Telford.

The engineers wasted little time and travelled to Bangor to blast off the surface of the Ynys y Moch site so it could be the foundation of one of the main piers. By 10th August, 1819, the first stone was laid without official ceremony even though two of the Commissioners, Sir Thomas Mostyn and Sir Henry Parnell were in the neighbourhood at the time. It was thought expedient to appear modest at this stage for opposition was still considerable.

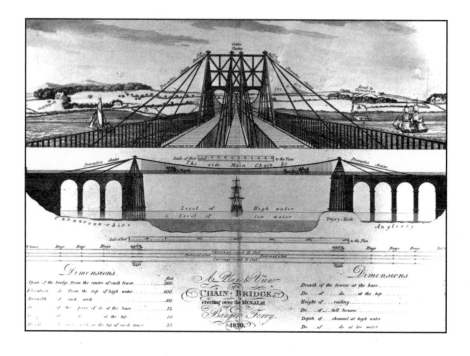

BOILING THE BRIDGE IN WINE

Telford was an engineer who began his working life as a stonemason, and the ironwork of the Menai Suspension Bridge caused him endless problems. The main difficulty was keeping the iron free of rust once it had left Hazeldean's foundry near Shrewsbury.

Lewis Carroll writing, 'Through the Looking Glass' often stayed in Llandudno and mentions it in the chapter called, 'It's my own invention':

White Knight says to Alice,
'I heard him then, for I had just
completed my design.
To keep the Menai Bridge from rust.
By boiling it in wine.'

Back at the Upton ironworks urgent tests were made and an answer was found to stop the rusting. Every piece of ironwork to be used, from a link in the main chains to a nut & bolt were cleaned as perfectly as possible of rust and dirt. They were then heated to a temperature that could just be touched by hand and plunged into linseed oil for five minutes. Later they were reheated until the oil dried to form a protecting coat of thin varnish.

When they arrived at Menai they could be stored without fear of corrosion. When needed the coat of oil was rubbed off.

THE STONEWORK

In the original construction of Pont y Borth *(the Menai Suspension Bridge)*, there were four chains riding over the main piers. Since its alteration in 1940, there are two. Telford had the problem of finding the best method of fastening these tremendous chains into the rock on either side of the Strait.

The way Telford did it was ingenious and simple. He drove three tunnels into the solid rock on either shore. This gave him two blocks of limestone and so by placing a large iron frame around these blocks he could fasten the chains.

The original contract for the masonry work was let to Messrs Stapleton and Hall, but because of difficulties they asked to be released from the contract. It was re-let to Mr John Wilson, one of Telford's principal contractors on the Caledonian Canal.

The limestone marble from the Penmon Quarries. The owner, Lord Viscount Warren Bulkeley was paid sixpence per ton for rough cut stone, by the Government. There were 80 men employed at the quarry to cut and ship the stone to the site at Menai.

The seven arches took four years to build and were completed in the autumn of 1824. The two principal piers are 153 feet high and carry the main chains. These main piers are hollow above high water mark. Telford considered it made the structure stronger. He said,

'One of the most important improvements, which I have been able to introduce into masonry, consists in the preference of cross-walls to rubble, in the structure of a pier, or any edifice requiring strength. Every stone and joint in such walls is open to inspection in the progress of the work, and even afterwards, if necessary; but a solid filling of rubble conceals itself, and may be little better than a heap of rubbish confined by side walls'.

Each stone is firmly bound together with mortar and iron dowels so as to withstand the immense pressure of the chains.

PUTTING UP THE CHAINS

With the stonework completed on both sides of the Strait and the chains laid from their moorings bedded in the rock to the top of the main towers, there remained the gap of 579 feet in between to be joined. The weight to be lifted was calculated, as was the power needed to raise a single chain 153 feet. How was it to be done?

There was a suggestion of stretching light iron wires in sufficient numbers to take the weight of a footway and a single chain. Once the first chain was up the other 15 could be raised fairly easily.

Telford decided to use a raft instead. It was 6 feet wide and 400 feet long and carried the first chain to hang over Afon Menai. The day chosen was the 26th April, 1825, to take advantage of a spring tide. Telford superintended the operation.

By noon a large crowd had gathered to watch something that had never happened before at Menai. At half past two the raft was given the signal to move away from its mooring at Treborth Mill and make its way to the main towers, a quarter of a mile away. It was then half flood tide.

This operation worried Telford considerably and he watched the boats pulling the pencil shaped raft. The mooring party stood by waiting to secure the chain to the Caernarfonshire main tower.

At the Anglesey end of the raft two blocks were fastened to the chain and hauled up and over the Anglesey tower by two capstans worked by 32 men. The chain lifted off the raft, and it floated away. The crowd cheered madly and Telford was so filled with emotion he knelt with tears in his eyes offering prayer and thanksgiving.

The first and most difficult of the chains had been raised successfully and the island of Anglesey was joined to the mainland. There were 15 more chains to be put into place and these were pulled up by pulley from the long raft. Ten weeks later by the 9th July, 1825, all the chains were up. After the final bolt had been fixed an astounding ceremony occurred.

Taking away the old chains for the new

The span held by temporary cables to remove the old chains

HEAVENLY BAND

A band playing from a platform high up on the Anglesey main pier marched down the chains on specially built planking to the centre and played the English National Anthem with the waters of the Menai Strait swirling 100 feet below.

These chains seem to inspire people into acts of devilment and daring. Just after the first one was put up in April 1825, three workmen, no doubt feeling rather excited with everybody cheering, ran along the chain from the Anglesey side to the main pier on the Caernarfonshire side. The crowd stopped cheering and gasped. The width of the swaying chain was only 9 inches wide. But the men made it safely, only to be reprimanded by Telford the next day.

There is an account of a cobbler who seems to have been affected by the excitement too. A local man told the story to a newspaper some time later. He wrote,

'Having been present as a boy from Bangor Grammar School, on the 26th April, when the first chain was carried across, an incident occurred which made no small impression on my mind at the time. After the chain had reached its position, a cobbler of the neighbourhood crawled to the centre of the curve and there finished a pair of shoes: when having completed his task, he returned in safety to the Caernarfon side. I need not say that we schoolboys appreciated his feat of foolhardiness far more than Telford's master work'.

ATTACHING THE ROADWAY

Work began in August 1825, to attach the roadway or main span to the chains. It was suspended from the chains by vertical rods one inch square. Each set of rods was placed five feet apart and was joined to iron sleepers which formed the basis of the roadway.

Across the sleepers three layers of deal planks were laid. The planking was spiked together and patent felt was laid between each plank. When the first layer of planks was down it enabled workmen to cross from one side to the other.

To celebrate the occasion a salute of 21 guns was fired from Craig y Don, the home of O. Williams, Esquire, M.P., and one of the Commissioners for the Holyhead Road improvements scheme. Once completed the two roads were separated by oak guards placed $7^1/_2$ feet apart, side railings were added and a toll-house built at each entrance to the bridge.

To allow for the lengthening of the chains in hot weather and subsequent dropping of the suspended roadway, the centre was 2 feet above the horizontal line.

There was no more to be done, except open Telford's masterpiece officially to the public.

THE OPENING

Pont y Borth *(the Menai Suspension Bridge)* was opened on Monday, 30th January, 1826. The great crowds which had gathered on both sides were soaked by the torrential rain which poured down steadily all morning. Fathers brought their sons so that they would remember this great day when they became men. They could say to their children, *'I sat on my father's shoulders and saw the very first coach to cross the Menai Strait'.*

By mid-day the rain eased to bring fine weather. At 1.35 a.m. the thousands of waiting and watching people cheered as the Royal London and Holyhead Mail Coach carrying the mail bags for Dublin crossed the Menai Suspension Bridge for the first time. It was manned by David Davies, coachman, and William Read, the guard. In the coach were Mr Hazeldean of Shrewsbury, very proud no doubt of his ironwork cast at Upton Forge, Mr Provis, the resident engineer, Mr Rhodes director of the timber, Mr J. Wilson and Mr W. Wilson, sons of the masonry contractor.

Following were two private carriages each drawn by elegant greys, tossing their heads, decorated with coloured ribbons. In the first carriage was Augustus Elliott Fuller, Esquire, one of the Commissioners. The second carriage carried Sir Henry Parnell and Thomas Telford. As they crossed a high wind made a whistling noise in the ironwork and the arches.

An old photograph of the bridge before reconstruction

THE PRESENT BRIDGE

The present structure is original only as far as the stonework is concerned. Between 1938 and 1941 the ironwork was completely replaced by steel to take the increased traffic.

Originally there was a weight limit of 4_ tons per vehicle and there were weigh bridges on each side. If a vehicle was overweight, it was particularly inconvenient as part of the load would have to be taken off and left behind. The vehicle would cross, take off more of its load, and return to the other side to replace the first load.

It was much the same with motor buses. If fully loaded, the conductor would yell out to his passengers 'Ten to walk the bridge', the bus would wait for walking passengers on the other side.

In windy weather the main span rolled and moved considerably. On one particularly stormy night in the winter of 1937, winds reached speeds of 60 miles per hour and the span swung out some 2 feet.

Messrs Dorman Long & Co. Limited were given the work of making Telford's bridge, built 100 years previously for horse carriages, strong enough to take twentieth century traffic. It was decided to renew the ironwork and span without stopping the traffic. The four main chains were replaced by two chains.

Two sets of seven wire cables were bound together to take the weight of old main span while the four old chains were removed. The two new chains were built in their place to hold the new deck which was underneath the old span.

Traffic was running over the old span all the time. This was cut lengthwise down the middle and one half taken away to enable half of the new span to be moved up. Traffic ran in single line on the old half, and then on half of the new deck.

The present bridge is designed to carry individual moving loads of 60 tons. The new chains weigh 1,300 tons and still go into the original tunnels made by Telford's men, but they have been deepened and widened for the new anchorages. When Dorman Long's engineers inspected the tunnels built over 100 years previously, they admired his ingenious method of anchoring the chains.

The work of reconstruction was considerable and was only half finished when war broke out in 1939. Work went on night and day, as German bombers passed overhead to raid Liverpool and Merseyside towns. On 31st December, 1940, it was opened officially and freed from toll.

Would Thomas Telford have approved of the alterations to his bridge? There is no doubt that the original construction with its four sets of chains instead of two was a more graceful structure. But Dorman Long are to be congratulated on fulfilling the modern requirement of a stronger bridge without losing the spirit of Telford's poem in stone and iron.

* * *

While Pont y Borth is the responsibility of the Ministry of Transport, it is Gwynedd County Council who act as agents and care for its day to day maintenance.

The maximum load the span can take is 400 tons. Any vehicle weighing over 32 tons has to have prior permission and a police escort.

The maximum number of vehicles recorded, on the electronic counting machine, in one day, is 33,000 in June 1971.

The bridge is painted overall every three years and takes some 300 gallons of paint, including an undercoat of red lead. Painting goes on constantly.

The stonework does not need a lot of attention but it is brushed with wire brushes occasionally. Clearing bird nests in high inaccessible places is a problem. Some rare bird nests have been found, e.g. a peregrine falcon and a sparrow hawk's nest.

Robin Richards' interesting book: *Two Bridges over Menai* reminded me vividly of the fire which seriously damaged Stevenson's Britannia Bridge creating complex problems for Anglesey its industries and communications. A serious additional burden was placed on Telford's suspension bridge and like so many others my weekly journey to and from London now involved travelling by train to Bangor then by bus to Llanfairpwllgwyngyll and vice versa.

Mr Idris Davies, Chief Executive of the Anglesey County Council held a weekly meeting on Friday at which the difficulties and prospects were discussed. Our main objective was to ensure that the bridge was repaired as quickly as possible. We were also concerned with the pressure on the suspension bridge. The possibility of a third bridge to relieve the pressure had been under consideration for some time. At one meeting when this was referred to, Mr Rowlands, the very able County Surveyor, said that a third bridge was no longer required. We all sat back in surprise and asked him to explain.

He then said that when Stevenson built the Britannia for the railway trains there was no alternative to a tubular structure. 'But today' said Mr William Rowlands, 'we can rebuild without the tubes and we can construct a road above the railway'. And so the great Britannia Tubular Bridge after much discussion and arguments assumed a new appearance and became Anglesey's second road bridge.

We owe a great deal to Mr William Rowlands.

The Right Hon. Lord Cledwyn of Penrhos PC, CH

THE BRITANNIA BRIDGE

THE BRITANNIA
– the bridge they thought was impossible to build

Robert Stephenson built Pont Britannia *(the Britannia Tubular Bridge)*. He was the son of a famous father, George Stephenson, the engineer who developed steam locomotives, notably the Rocket. George Stephenson predicted:

'The time will come when it will be cheaper for a working man to make a journey by railway than to walk on foot.'

Before 1830 towns grew along riverbanks but this changed with the development of railways. Stephenson's locomotives brought dramatic changes to the western world, in a single generation. Canadian and American wealth was opened up to trade and settlement. Railways carried goods cheaply and at a speed horse drawn coaches could never match. Through railways, cheap postage was possible.

George Stephenson, self-educated engineer and inventor of the safety lamp, had to fight the social and professional prejudice of the civil engineers of his day. His ideas were ridiculed as *'moonshine'* and yet, in spite of everything, he proved them wrong.

And so it was with Robert the son, and the Britannia Tubular Bridge. This was the bridge that was impossible to build.

Britannia Bridge by G Hawkins

31

STEPHENSON'S CHOICE

The problem was to open a railway to Dublin. There were two possible routes – through Holyhead, Anglesey, which meant crossing the Menai Strait or through a new harbour at Porthdinllaen near Nefyn, in Llŷn.

Stephenson the father was commissioned in 1838, by the Chester and Crewe Company, to survey both possibilities. He came out strongly in favour of going through Holyhead because it presented better gradients and was less costly.

A public meeting was held at Chester in January 1839, at which Stephenson gave explanations for his choice. Mr Uniacke, the mayor, was biased in favour of the Holyhead crossing and dismissed the rival Porthdinllaen route as *'quite impracticable'*. The latter would have meant that Shrewsbury and not Chester would have been the main junction for Ireland.

One questioner at the Chester meeting asked Stephenson how he proposed crossing the Menai Strait. He said something extremely interesting: *'I propose to convey railway carriages across Telford's suspension road bridge'.*

The proposal was to take trains up to Telford's road bridge and uncouple the locomotive. The railway carriages could then be drawn across the suspension bridge by horses. This overcame the insoluble problem of keeping a bridge rigid while a train passed over. It also saved them building another bridge.

While this did not actually happen in 1850, a similar idea was used in 1970. Following the disastrous fire to the Britannia Railway Bridge, British Rail had locomotives and rolling stock trapped on Anglesey. Stranded coaches were taken by road across the Telford Bridge. The clearance of a passenger coach crossing the bridge was a mere five inches.

By 1844, the objections from local preservationists, from the Holyhead lobby and from the Porthdinllaen lobby were brought to an end by an Act of Parliament. There were many modifications.

The work originally started by George Stephenson the father was completed by Robert his son. They proposed the original idea of bridging the Menai Strait and the Conwy estuary with tubular bridges. They also put forward a remarkable terrace cutting to take a railway under a steep slope which hangs above the sea at Penmaenmawr.

The biggest difficulty was the problem of crossing the Menai Strait. Thomas Telford had succeeded only twenty-five years previously in 1826, but Robert Stephenson had an even greater problem. It was one thing to bridge the Strait – it was, however, another to build a bridge that would keep stiff enough to take a locomotive and train. Also Telford had taken the best and shortest crossing point.

Robert Stephenson first suggested an iron-arched railway bridge but this was rejected by the Admiralty because it would interfere with the navigation of the Menai Strait. There was formidable opposition from those wanting the Porthdinllaen route and they had persuaded the Admiralty to obtain a report on the navigational dangers. It worried Stephenson to such an extent that he is reported to have said: *'I stood, therefore, on the verge of a responsibility from which I confess I had nearly shrunk'*.

Robert Stephenson went back to his plans. There seemed no answer to the problem of crossing Afon Menai with a bridge that would remain rigid in all weather conditions and carry a locomotive, train and passengers safely.

Stephenson's cast iron arch proposal as the Britannia Bridge

AS STRONG AS STRAW

He thought of a design he had made for a bridge in 1841, on the Hertford and Ware branch of the Northern and Eastern Railway. It was a wrought-iron platform consisting of a number of cells with the boiler plates riveted together by angle-irons. Slowly the idea came to him that this principle was the answer: build a pair of tubes big enough to take trains, supported in mid-air by strong towers.

As a precaution, he thought the tubes could be supported by chains. But a significant event in Blackwall occurred which increased Stephenson's faith in the strength of the tubes.

Stephenson's theory was proven beyond doubt when news came of the launching of an iron steamship at Blackwall, called the 'Prince of Wales'. As the ship was being launched she stuck and stopped with 110 feet of her hull suspended above the water for some considerable time.

It was thought that the tremendous weight of her hull would put so much strain on the plates as to buckle them. But the plates did not buckle. It proved the strength of a tube – for that in principle is what a ship's hull is.

When Stephenson announced his proposal for a tubular bridge, it was greeted with incredulity. And yet the strength of tubes has been known to nature all along.

Consider a reed or length of straw and notice how strong they are in relation to the very small amount of material contained in them. A tube of any material is stronger than the same amount rolled into a solid rod of less diameter.

Robert Stephenson asked an engineer, William Fairbairn, to make experiments with various materials. Fairbairn tested tubes of all dimensions: egg-shaped, circular, square and rectangular, all with or without chain support. He eventually developed a rectangular shaped tube strengthened with hollow cells at the top and bottom.

Erection of the masonary towers for the Britannia Bridge

THE FIRST TUBULAR BRIDGE

So began the beginning of a completely original idea in bridge building and the first tubular bridge was to be built over Afon Menai. When the news reached Robert Stephenson, he contacted two old friends of his father – William Fairbairn an engineer and ship-builder, and Professor Eaton Hodgkinson an authority on iron beams, Stephenson set them to work on reporting the feasibility of building a tubular bridge. They came up with two differing opinions.

Hodgkinson said:

'If it be determined to erect a bridge of tubes, I would beg to recommend that suspension chains be employed as an auxiliary.'

A view of the northern masonry and tubular approaches showing the scaffolding and tube fitted into the Anglesey and Britannia piers

Fairbairn recommended:

'Provided the parts are well proportioned, and the plates properly riveted, you may strip off the chains . . . '

Stephenson had to choose between two conflicting opinions from eminent men. It worried him greatly. He admitted to a friend:

'Often at night I would lie tossing about seeking sleep in vain. The tubes filled my head. I went to bed with them and got up with them. In the grey of the morning when I looked across the square it seemed an immense distance across to the houses on the opposite side. It was nearly the same length as the span of my bridge.'

In the end Stephenson backed William Fairbairn's judgement and decided to build a tubular bridge without supporting chains – such was his faith in the strength of a tube.

A one-sixth size model was built at Fairbairn's shipyard at Millwall. It measured 75ft between bearings, 4ft 6ins deep and 2ft 8ins wide. Breaking tests were carried out so that the eventual load was 86 tons before the plates tore apart. With these results the construction of the final tubes could begin.

WHO WAS JP?

These remarkable photographs are unique because they were taken in 1849 – one year before the Britannia bridge was opened. The first known photograph of the second Crystal Palace did not appear until four years later in 1853-54.

These pictures appeared in the offices of Sir Alexander Gibb & Partners of Cardiff. They were presented to Powysland museum. This museum is one of the oldest antiquarian societies in Britain. It is maintained by Welshpool Town Council. Research suggests the photographs were taken by the same person 'half a mile from the sight at about noon'. There could be more such photographs around.

Two have the initials JP.

Who was JP?

An article in the 'New Civil Engineer' dated August 1987 offers two names. The first – J. Price of Plas Cadnant, Menai Bridge and J. Pring – surgeon of Bangor.

The photographer still remains as mysterious as these remarkable three photographs.

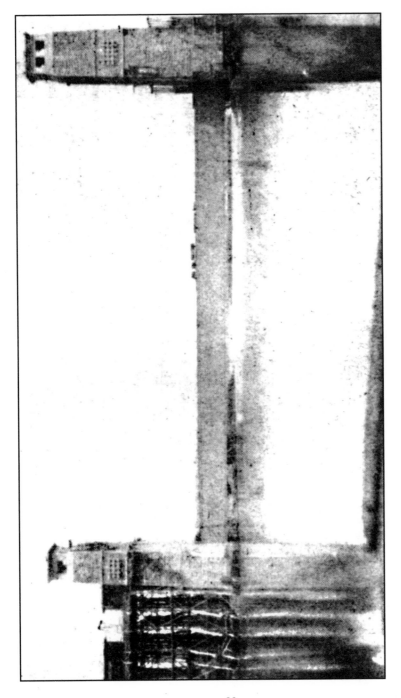

The southern pier of the tubular bridge. The base is incomplete waiting for the tubes so that they can be floated into place for lifting

The southern pier shows an incomplete base ready to receive the tubes when floated into the recess for lifting

INFERNAL DUELS

The quiet banks of the Menai Strait were transformed into what amounted to a wooden town inhabited solely by working men and youths – riveters, engineers, carpenters, blacksmiths, painters and labourers. They came from just about every part of the British Isles in search of work at Menai.

There were boys of ten-years of age employed as rivet boys. The boys had the job of carrying white hot rivets from the forges in long pincers. Being boys, they were mischievous and were not averse to the occasional slight nudge at one another with a hot rivet. A report of one eye witness reads:

'The rivet boys, generally unintentionally, but occasionally, it is said, from pure mischief, burn each other more or less severely, in which cases a couple of these suckling vulcans, utterly unable, from incessant noise, to quarrel by words, fall to blows and have even been observed to fight a sort of infernal duel with pincers, each trying to burn his opponent anywhere and everywhere with his red-hot bolt'.

The top of each rectangular tube was strengthened by putting on another layer. The distance between the top layer and its inner layer was 21 inches in depth and 20 inches wide – just enough for a man and a rivet boy to crawl on their stomachs to hold one plate underneath while a rivet head was banged into position.

One dramatic sight was to see the rivet boys throw their red-hot rivets some forty feet into the air to be caught by the rivet gangs on top of the tubes. In all, 900 tons of rivet iron were used. The contribution made by these children has too often been overlooked.

On the banks of Afon Menai at the site of the bridge were 3_ acres of huts, offices and living quarters.

The weight of the tubes, each about 1,500 tons, was so great that the supporting timber staging began collapsing and Stephenson had to strengthen it by driving in wedges.

The technical expertise, at that time, for producing wrought iron plate was primitive. Every piece of plating had to be flattened by hand with 40 lb. sledge-hammers. When this process was finished, the rivet holes were punched through. It took a team months of banging with 40 lb. hammers to flatten the $3^1/_2$ inch bedplates.

Rivetting one of the Britannia Bridge tubes

AN AMAZING CONCERT

A month before the floating of the first tube in June 1849, there appeared an account of what must have been an amazing musical concert. The North Wales Chronicle story is called 'Concert Extraordinary'.

'Friday evening, (18th May, 1849), a Concert was given to the whole country round by the Engineering Staff at headquarters connected with the Chester and Holyhead Railway in the great centre tube of the Britannia bridge which was brilliantly lighted up in the centre length, lined with branches at the entrance to resemble a grove, with seats run along the sides for the promenaders to rest them.

'The vocal ability of Caernarfon and Bangor were in full force on this occasion, assisted by Mr Hayden of St Mary's of the former place, who accompanied on the melodium. The "corps musicale" consisted of 40 or more vocalists and allowing for the diluting effects upon the human voice of a chamber containing from 700 to 800 persons, with an area of upwards 470 feet long, better adapted to the saxhorns of the Distin family – the concert went off with as much eclat as could fairly have been may say all were struck with the novelty of the thing; while few could have had any previous conception of the brilliant spectacle presented by the illuminated tube and the animated countenances on which its coruscation fell.'

FLOATING THE FIRST TUBE

While the tubes were being constructed the stonework on the three towers was being built. Ships brought red sandstone for the interior masonry from Runcorn, Cheshire and Anglesey limestone for the exterior work from Penmon.

The foundation stone was laid by the resident engineer, Mr Frank Foster, on 10th April, 1846. By July 1847, he was able to report that the masonry work was progressing rapidly. As with the ironwork, there was tremendous activity with the blasting of rock and trimming of the stone, night and day. By June 1849 the stone piers were ready to receive the first 472ft long tube. It lay waiting on the banks of the Menai ready to be lifted 100 feet. Stephenson's problem was how to do it.

The way Stephenson solved the problem has fascinated bridge builders ever since. Everything about the Britannia bridge was unique. It was the first time a rectangular tube had been used to carry not just people and horses but a double track railway; and never had a length of tube 472 feet long weighing 1,500 tons been lifted 100 feet.

It was a man called Evans, the contractor for the Conwy railway bridge, who convinced Stephenson that the best way of erecting the tubes was to build them on shore and then float them to the stone piers for lifting.

While Telford had floated the suspension chains for the Menai Suspension Bridge, they only weighed $23^1/_2$ tons each.

Stephenson decided to have a dress rehearsal at the Conwy railway bridge in March 1848, with tubes weighing 1,000 tons. Things did not go well – there were delays because of foul weather and there were serious accidents. Pontoons were swept out of position and ended up on the banks.

Stephenson had even greater problems facing him at the Britannia site at Menai. He went over every possible difficulty – even to the extent of building a model of the Britannia Tubular Bridge, to the scale of one inch to 6ft.

On the evening of 19th June, 1849, the first tube was ready to be floated. Both sides of the Menai Strait were lined with excited people. On the Caernarfon side, the three other constructed tubes were turned into grandstands so that the crowd could see all that was happening. The cannon that saluted Telford, was ready to do the same for Stephenson.

On the Anglesey side near Llanfairpwllgwyngyll, the Chester and Holyhead Company directors had a special stand. Stephenson invited his old friend Brunel to witness the great occasion.

Stephenson gave the order at 6.00 p.m. to cut away the pontoons but, unfortunately, the whole affair was spoiled by the breaking of a capstan. A disappointed crowd on both sides of the Strait melted away. But they were back next morning to see the big tube lifted with their help.

The wind was high and the tide particularly vicious at that part of the Strait. The efforts of the sailors to get the pontoon hauling lines laid out were in vain. The weather played havoc with buoys and some small boats were smashed and sunk.

Stephenson witnessed this all day and doggedly gave the order at 7.30 p.m. to 'cut away'. The great tube began to move towards the stone piers but the wind and tide were still strong; its speed began to increase alarmingly. Stephenson ordered the screw cable-stoppers to check the tube's speed. They failed when an 8 inch check cable snapped. For a few minutes, 1,500 tons of iron was in danger of being swept down the Menai Strait to disaster. In addition there was near panic on the Anglesey shore.

It was intended to guide the Anglesey end of the tube so that it was placed against the base of the Anglesey pier. It could then swing on an axis until the other end was secured to the centre pier. The guiding cable was operated from a capstan at Plas Llanfair on the Anglesey shore. The 12 inch cable jammed the capstan and it was wrenched from its foundations, throwing some of the men working it, into the Strait.

The man in charge of this capstan, Foreman Charles Rolfe, had great presence of mind. He shouted to the crowd for help. Men, women and children took hold of the cable and pulled in possibly the most desperate tug of war ever.

En masse, they were dragged by the big tube moving down the Strait. They must have thought they would be pulled into the water. And then they found they were not being dragged any more, and the tube went into its proper place at the base of the tower. How they cheered as the cannon fired a salute.

It was reported at the time, that Stephenson turned to Brunel and said, *'Now – I shall go to bed'*.

Floating out the one of the Britannia tubes

INCH BY INCH

The task of raising the tube was one which Stephenson treated cautiously. Two hydraulic pumps, which had raised the tubes at Conwy, were brought to Menai and installed in the Britannia pier.

Stephenson had a team of young and enthusiastic assistants. His resident engineer, Edwin Clark and the assistants, wanted to raise the tube right away. They approached Stephenson saying, *'We could get it up to its full height within two days'*.

Stephenson did not agree, for he remembered one of the things that went wrong at Conwy when the second tube was being lifted into position. When only 2ft 3 inches short of its correct height, Stephenson noticed a crack, inches long, in one of the lifting pumps. The pump tackle weighing 50 tons collapsed. It killed one man and damaged the tube. Through good fortune, the fractured pump held long enough for the tube it was holding to be packed and underpinned.

Stephenson remembered how this accident had put back work 6 weeks. He insisted that there would be no rushing the Britannia lift. His reply to his young engineers was:

'No. You must only raise the tube inch by inch, and you must build up under it as it rises. Every inch must be made good. Nothing must be left to chance or good luck.'

It was lucky that he insisted on complete caution. One day when the hydraulic pumps were at work, the bottom of one pump virtually disintegrated. Its chains and crosshead weighing 50 tons fell on the pump. The tube fell a mere 9 inches, yet it crushed solid castings, weighing tons. Luckily the slip only damaged the tube slightly.

Stephenson's caution had proved right and Edwin Clark wrote to him saying:

'Thank God you have been so obstinate. If this accident had occurred without a bed for the end of the tube to fall on, the whole would now have been laying across the bottom of the Strait'.

This accident cost an extra £5,000, and the lifting gear was improved.

The accuracy with which the tube had been built was such that, when it was raised, it fitted into the slot, on the stone pier with three quarters of an inch to spare.

The work progressed until the three other tubes were raised in the same way. The tubes are fixed into the centre tower and ride on brass bearings in the two smaller towers. The tubes, joining the shore to the smaller piers on both sides, were built on scaffolding. The second tube was floated on 3rd December and raised on 7th January, 1850: the other two were put into place shortly afterwards.

Conwy tubular bridge

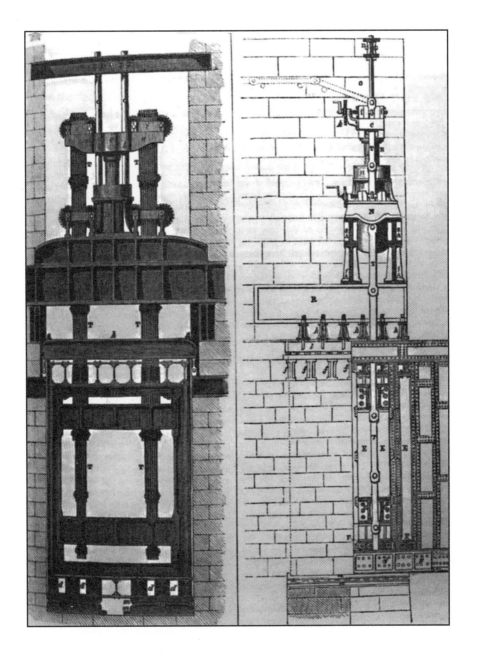

Section at the tube end showing the hydraulic presses

THE LIONS

These were designed by the Victorian sculptor, John Thomas, who was architect to the new Houses of Parliament. They are made out of carboniferous limestone, hewn from the nearby quarry at Penmon.

There is a pair at each end of the bridge and have been described as *'two pairs of sphinx-like lions'*. It has been suggested that the bridge itself has a Graeco-Egyptian design. The lions were regarded as symbolizing the strength of the bridge. They each measure 25ft 6 inches in length and are 12ft 8 inches high. Their width across the body is some 9ft and the width of each paw is 2ft 4 inches. The amount of stone used is 80 tons. Each lion is made of 11 pieces.

They are typical examples of the ornamental frills of their time and to us today are possibly not very inspiring.

It was intended to have a colossal 60ft high figure of Brittania put on top of the centre tower complete with trident and shield, but luckily high costs and providence prevented its construction.

An eccentric Anglesey bard, from Porthaethwy *(Menai Bridge)*, had the habit of writing poems on any contemporary event and sending his pearls to Queen Victoria. He was slightly mad but loveable character, whom the local inhabitants christened 'Y Bardd Cocos' *(the Cockle Bard)*. When he saw the huge lions he put pen to paper and wrote the following piece of delightful nonsense rhyme about them in Welsh:

Two lions thin	Dau lew tew
Two lions fat	Heb ddim blew,
Two on this side	Dau'r ochor yma
Two on that.	A dau'r ochor drew.

The lions in place before the fire

FINISHED AND OPENED

Stephenson put the last rivet in the tube at a ceremony on 5th March, 1850. He rode through his completed masterpiece in a train carrying some 1,000 passengers drawn by three locomotives. During the same day a train carrying 200 tons of coal was stopped in the centre of the eastern land tube. Checks were made for strain and a deflection of only four-tenths of an inch was found. The safety margin allowed a deflection of 13 inches.

The bridge was opened for public traffic on 18th March, 1850.

THE BRIDGE IS ON FIRE

It happened on the evening of Saturday, 23rd May, 1970.

Within half an hour, the Press teleprinters revealed that Stephenson's Britannia Tubular Bridge was ablaze from end to end.

Sixty firemen from Caernarfon and Anglesey brigades fought the blaze for seven hours into the early morning, before they were forced to retreat from the flames.

A train on its way from Caergybi *(Holyhead)* was stopped in time, by signals, before it reached the burning bridge.

By next morning every newspaper in Wales & England carried banner headlines: *'Bridge blaze cuts link – Prime Minister calls in Ministers to speed Rail Re-opening'* – Western Mail.

Emergency arrangements were made to ferry boat-train passengers by bus between Bangor and Holyhead. Boat trains were re-routed to Heysham.

An Anglesey fire officer is reported as saying:

'The iron roof was red-hot in places and it was like an inferno inside. We were nearly gassed and the hose nozzles were almost red-hot.'

On the following day, a Sunday, police had to control large crowds of sightseers who had come to see the still smouldering bridge, its towers blackened and ironwork blistered by the tremendous heat.

The estimated damage amounted to £2 million with even higher losses for British Rail. The effect was disastrous for Anglesey's economy and especially for Holyhead.

The cost to the people of Holyhead meant that many found themselves out of work. It was expected that 300 workers would be put on the dole. British Rail announced just four weeks after the fire on 29th June, 1970:

'Men will be laid off because rail traffic has been stopped and some 222 men in the shipping division and about 50 in the rail division are affected.'

The Minister of Transport, Mr Mulley, was summoned to 10

Downing Street to confer with the Prime Minister, Harold Wilson. Mr Mulley met the Secretary of State for Wales George Thomas, Anglesey's M.P. Cledwyn Hughes and British Rail's chief executive.

They inspected the charred and buckled tubes. The iron beams had expanded in the heat and then contracted to such an extent that they had broken. They were in danger of falling off the stone towers. No 8 Field Squadron of the Royal Engineers were sent to Menai, and immediately set about averting disaster by building Bailey bridges underneath as temporary supports.

By July, the promised job redundancies had taken place. A meeting in the town demanded to see the Secretary of State for Wales, the Minister of Transport, their M.P. and the chairman of the British Rail Board.

A suggestion that the word *'demand'* be changed to 'request' was shouted down. *'They are the servants of the people – let them come and serve us. Let Ted Heath the Prime Minister come himself,'* said one person.

Reconstruction of the Britannia Bridge in the 1970's.

PREFABRICATION

Port Dinorwig harbour, two miles south of the bridge was chosen for the prefabrication of the arch units.

The harbour bottom was filled in and levelled carefully so pontoons could be accurately and firmly grounded at low tide alongside the dock wall. There were eight erection buoys, each holding two arch units. Completed arch units were floated at high tide and anchored near to the bridge. Departures were timed so that units arrived in slack water. Lifting ropes were attached until the next slack water and the unit was lifted clear.

Beginning to put up the supporting arch

HOW IT HAPPENED

Five young people aged 15, 16 and 17 set out to attend a party at nearby Penrhos. As the girl, to whose house they went, was not at home, they wandered down to the entrance of the Britannia Bridge.

They thought they heard some bats near the tunnel entrance, but discovered there were some birds on a girder behind a wall on the right-hand side of the tunnel.

It was dark in the tunnel; and one of the group found an old magazine on the floor, tore out a page and held it while another boy lighted it with a cigarette lighter. They held the burning paper behind the girder but could see nothing. At that moment they heard a woman call. The piece of burning paper dropped down into the space behind the girder and the youths ran out of the tunnel.

They decided to go back to the girl's house where the party was to have been held. As they ran away they heard the woman shouting, *'The bridge is on fire'*.

The old and new Britannia bridges

THE FUTURE

British Rail have spent some £3,250,000 on rebuilding. This is in excess of the figure given at the time of the fire; but is explained by the new design which allows for the provision of a road deck over the railway track suitable for carrying a three-lane road.

This road is at the request of the Secretary of State for Wales. The Welsh Office agreed to pay £400,000 for the extra work involved. The new road has now been constructed.

The bridge only carries a single track, but automatic track circuiting, enables twelve trains an hour to cross the bridge.

Reconstruction was divided into four stages Stephenson's original stonework remaining.

1. Steel lattice arches were used to support the two water spans and stanchions to support the two land spans. The temporarily supported north tube was then used for rail traffic.
2. The south tube was removed.
3. A permanent rail track was then built on the site of the present south tube and traffic transferred from the north tube in December 1973.
4. The north tube was being removed during the course of 1974.

Consultant engineers are Husband and Co, who have designed the new bridge and have employed Cleveland Engineering Ltd of Darlington for the construction work.

The first train across the bridge after the fire went on 30th January, 1972. The link between Holyhead and Ireland was re-established after a break of twenty months. Holyhead celebrated with a display of fireworks when the M/V Cambria arrived at her moorings. Councillor Hugh Jones, chairman of Holyhead Council tied the ship's hawser to a bollard, while the Holyhead Silver Band played.

Constructing the steel arches for the new Britannia bridge.

The new Britannia bridge

Fabricating the original Britannia tubes

PONT Y BORTH (MENAI SUSPENSION BRIDGE)

ft

Height of the two main piers from high water line
to the level of the road-way 100

Height of the two main piers from the level
of the road-way to the top 53

Width of each main pier at high-water mark 42

Thickness of each main pier at high-water mark 60

Height of arches in main piers, through which the
carriage roads pass, reckoning to spring of arch 15

Width of ditto 9

Height of each of the small piers from high-water line
to the spring of the arches 65

Span of each of the seven arches 52

Length of each chain from fastenings in the rock 1714

Length of the suspended portion of each chain
between the main piers, forming a curvature 590

Length of road-ways suspended between main piers 550

Total length of road-way 1000

Width of each road-way 12

Width of the foot-path between the road-ways 4

No. of chains – 16; No. of chain-bars in each chain-plate – 935; No. of chains which unite the chain-bars in each chain – 1122; No. of bolts in each chain – 374; Total No. vertical rods in the four lines of suspension – 796.

Total weight of each chain – 121 tons, 1282 lbs. The suspending power of the chains is calculated at 2016 tons; as the whole weight of the suspended portion of the bridge is 489 tons, the available power is 1527 tons.

The cost of the entire structure was about £120,000.

The first stone was laid on the 10th August, 1819, and the bridge opened to the public on 30th January, 1826.

Engineer: Mr Telford

PONT BRITANNIA (BRITANNIA TUBULAR BRIDGE)

Dimensions of the LONG TUBES

	ft	in.
Depth of tubes at centre tower	30	0
Depth of tubes at extreme ends	23	0
Width of tubes from outside to outside	14	8
Length of tubes, 472ft; when up	488	8
Height of Tubes above high-water	100	0
Height of Tubes above low-water	121	6
Weight of each tube	1800tns	
Each tube contains 327,000 rivets, whole	2,000,000	

Dimensions of the SHORT TUBES

	ft	in.
Depth of tubes at tower end	27	0
Depth of tube at the abutment	23	0
Width of tubes from outside to outside	14	8
Length of tubes 230ft; total length	266	0
(including their hold upon the masonry)		
Length of the entire bridge	1834	3
Weight of each tube	700 tns.	
Weight of malleable iron in the tubes	10,000 do.	

The MASONRY

Britannia Tower 62ft by 52ft 5ins in the base
Where the tubes enter, 55ft by 45ft 5ins
Total height – 230ft

It contains 148,625 cubic feet of limestone, 144,625 of sandstone: Weighing nearly 20,000 tons; there are 387 tons of cast iron built in it in the shape of beams.

They are each 25ft 6ins in length, and 12ft 8ins in height, though crouched; breadth across the body is about 9ft; breadth of each paw, 2ft 4ins. They contain about 8,000 cubic feet of stone; weighing 80 tons.

Bridge opened for Traffic 21st October, 1850.
Total cost of structure is officially stated at £621,865.
The first Tube floated on 20th June, 1849, and the last on 25th July, 1850.

Engineer: Mr R. Stephenson

(These two pages are taken from a card which was originally printed towards the end of the 19th Century.)